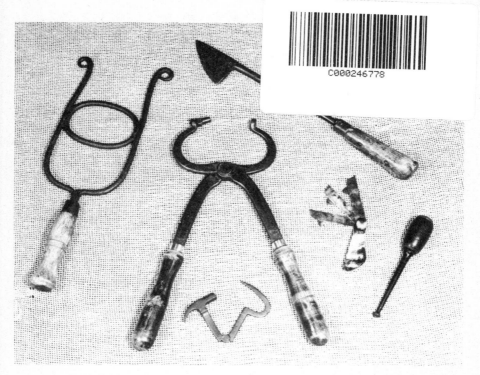

ABOVE AND COVER: *A selection of some of the veterinary bygones described in this book.*

THE COUNTRY ANIMAL DOCTOR

Arthur Ingram

Photographs by Malcolm Harris

Shire Publications Ltd

CONTENTS

Printed in Great Britain by C. I. Thomas & Sons (Haverfordwest) Ltd, Press Buildings, Merlins Bridge, Haverfordwest.

Obstetrical forceps used by shepherds to assist in a difficult lambing.

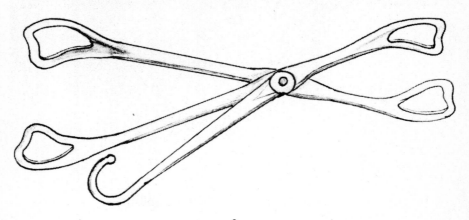

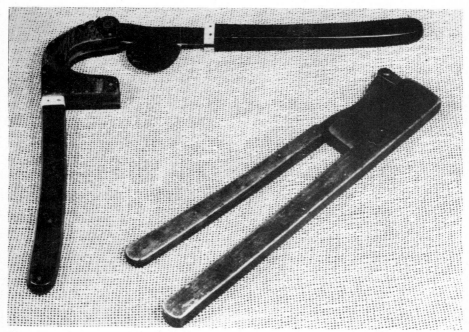

Two horse tail-docking irons. The open one was finely made by a veterinary instrument maker, while the closed example is of simpler rural origin.

INTRODUCTION

In 1948 the Veterinary Surgeons Act appeared on the statute book, stipulating that henceforth all who wished to practise veterinary medicine should be members of the Royal College of Veterinary Surgeons and have undergone a lengthy period of exacting training and examinations, qualifying them to place the letters MRCVS after their name. A provision was made, however, that those not so qualified but who had been operating as veterinary practitioners up to that time would be permitted to continue their practices.

Thus veterinary medicine became the preserve of the professional, but in the past all manner of persons had performed their versions of animal doctoring. In the nineteenth century qualified veterinary surgeons plied their craft alongside laymen. The farrier acted as vet in most villages, particularly in regard to horses, although the carter frequently treated his own. The stockman, pigman and shepherd treated their own animals, as did many cottagers. The local quack would eke out a modest living by prescribing cures that seldom worked, and some village worthy with keenly honed clasp knife would be prepared to neuter his neighbour's tom cat for a small consideration. Forms of chicanery bordering on the black arts were practised by a few individuals who exhibited strange powers over horses and were known to country folk as horse whisperers.

Many unlikely and fascinating instruments were evolved to aid the animal doctor, layman or professional, in his task. A few have survived to the present day.

3

ABOVE: *A set of casting hobbles fitted to a horse.*

BELOW: *The horse cast, with all four feet drawn together, and being fitted with a blinder.*

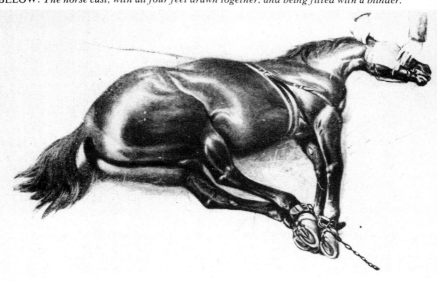

4

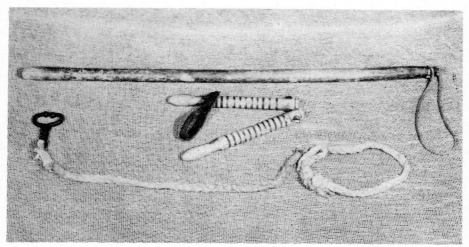

A twitch (top) looped round a horse's top lip enabled the animal to be restrained. A mouth cramp (centre) was also attached to the horse's lip for the same purpose. The bulldog clamp (bottom), attached to a rope, would have been fitted into a cow's nostrils.

RESTRAINT

The first problem encountered in treating any ailing animal was that the animal could not understand that the treatment was for its own benefit. The treatment of a large, powerful animal was almost impossible because of its constant struggles to free itself. Many devices were used to combat this problem.

One of the simplest of these, used with horses, consisted of a loop of string attached to a short pole. It was called a *twitch*. The string was looped around the horse's tender upper lip and, by twisting the pole, was tightened to grip the flesh firmly. It was applied to the tongue by some but this was incorrect and could injure the animal. An alternative instrument was the *mouth cramp*. Two rounded bars of wood, 12 inches long (300mm) and hinged at one end, were clamped to the top lip and secured tightly with a leather thong. With either of these devices one man could usually restrain the most powerful horse. Used correctly, they inflicted just enough discomfort to dissuade the animal from adding to it by struggling but caused far less distress than at-

tempting to subdue it by physical force. However, for major surgery a horse did often need to be restrained more forcefully, and this was done by throwing it on its side, an operation known as *casting*. The more professional way of doing this was with *hobbles*. These were stout leather straps buckled around each of the four pasterns. Each buckle had a steel ring and through these rings a rope was passed. When the rope was pulled towards the rear of the horse all four legs were drawn together, toppling the animal on to its side. When it was down its eyes were usually covered with a canvas hood, called a blinder, to prevent injury. A more homespun method of casting was done with a wagon rope. It was looped around the horse's neck and run out in two slack loops diagonally to opposing hind legs (left side of neck to right hind leg and *vice versa*). The loops were placed around the pasterns and the end was passed through a ring in the neck band. Pulling from the rear, the handler dragged the hind legs forward and inward. When cast, the horse was often further restrained by sacks of

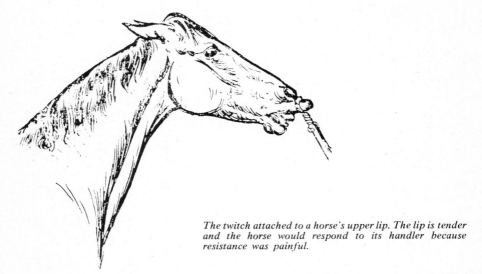

The twitch attached to a horse's upper lip. The lip is tender and the horse would respond to its handler because resistance was painful.

grain placed upon it.

When collapsed from some debilitating ailment and unable to gain its feet. a horse was often raised in a *sling*, a contraption of canvas and leather straps passed under the belly and raised by means of ropes and pulley blocks. It was seldom used for cattle because it was likely to damage their complex digestive system. Also cattle will live for weeks without rising, provided they are lying upright, but a horse will survive on the ground for only a few days.

A horse with an injured flank would often aggravate the wound by turning and nibbling at it. To prevent this, it was often fitted with a *horse cradle*. This device consisted of between six and ten wooden rods about 16 inches (400mm) long, strung on two lengths of cord passing through holes at either end. This cord also passed through wooden spacers about 3 inches (75mm) long which kept the rods that distance apart. The front ends of the rods were sharpened to a point. The cradle was hung around the horse's neck like a collar, the rods lying horizontally, and frustrated the horse's efforts to turn its head round to its flank.

Crib-biting and its attendant condition, wind-sucking, had disastrous effects on a horse's system. These conditions were countered either by fitting a tight leather strap around the neck or by a heavy leather *night muzzle*, similar to that fitted to dogs.

Cattle could often be restrained simply by looping a rope around the horns and throwing it over a convenient beam. An alternative was the *bulldog* or *nose clamp*. This was a spring-loaded pincer which fitted into the cow's nostrils. One type was fitted to a rope and was used over a beam to haul the head upwards to administer medicines. Another was fitted to short pincer handles or a simple ring handle. This type was commonly called a *bull-leader* and was used for normal restraint.

Powerful aggressive bulls were fitted with copper nose rings. A hole was punched in the cartilage between the nostrils with a *nose punch*, a pincer-like device with a circular cutting edge which removed a core. The hinged ring was placed through the hole, closed and secured by a small screw. By clipping a *bull pole* or *staff* on to this, the bull could be comfortably controlled, relying on the same principle as with the twitch mentioned earlier. Bulls which became very aggressive or 'rafty', as they were described in country areas, were occasionally fitted with a *bull blind*. Looking rather like an ancient warrior's breast-plate, it could be either of stout leather or metal and was strapped on so that it completely covered the beast's forehead,

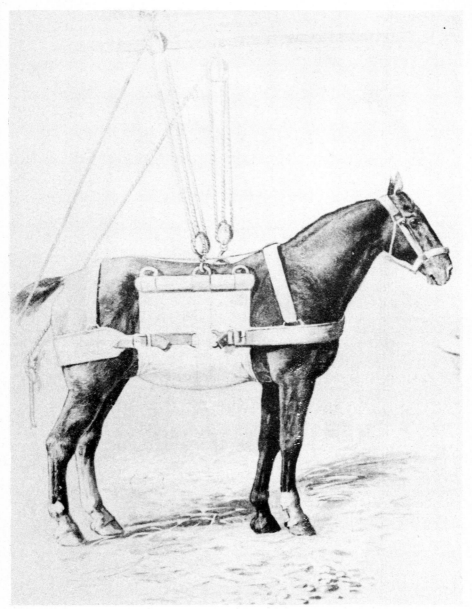

A horse suspended in a sling by means of ropes and pulleys. This device was used to keep horses upright because they will die if left lying down, unable to stand, for more than a few days.

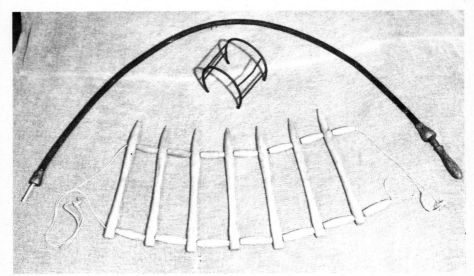

The flexible probang (top) was used to remove blockages from a cow's throat. The sheep collar (centre) was fastened to the animal's neck to prevent it from bending its head to nibble a wound on its flank. The horse cradle (bottom) served the same purpose for horses.

curving around either side to obscure the eyes. The theory was that what the bull could not see it would not charge, but it was not the most successful of aids. One old stockman, who remembered seeing it used, recalled: 'It made 'n a damn zite wuss!'

Pigs can be the most troublesome creatures to control, as apart from the ears there is little to grasp and they are notoriously easy to choke. Probably the most effective way of securing them is with a rope noose around the upper jaw.

Sheep are normally light enough to be handled with ease. However, a truculent ram could prove difficult and in this case the shepherd used a *sheep yoke* consisting of the fork of a sapling cut from the hedgerow, with a hole bored in each branch to take a wooden pin. The sheep's head was placed in the V and the pin was slid across above the nape of its neck, making withdrawal of its head impossible. This device could be either permanently embedded in the floor of a shearing shed or portable, being hammered into the ground wherever the need arose. Another aid used for the same purpose was the *shepherd's mate*, a rectangular wooden frame with steel-tipped points extending from its lower corners, enabling it to be driven into the ground. Fixed by a pivot at a bottom corner and running diagonally across the frame was another wooden bar, which formed a V with one of the uprights. This bar could be pulled tight to the sheep's neck, where it was retained by a metal pin.

Sheep were also given to nibbling wounds on their flanks and were often fitted with a semicircular iron frame called a *sheep collar*. This dropped on to the neck and was secured beneath with leather thongs. Like the horse cradle, it prevented the head being turned.

A similar principle has long been used on cats and dogs for the same reason. A

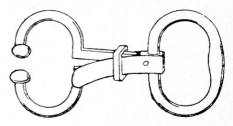

A bull leader was fitted to the animal's nostrils and enabled it to be controlled.

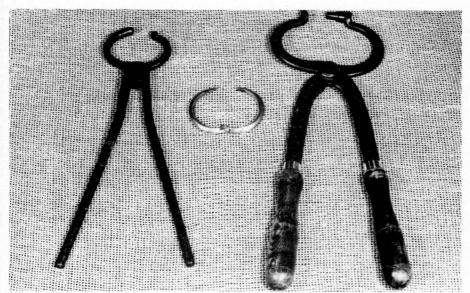

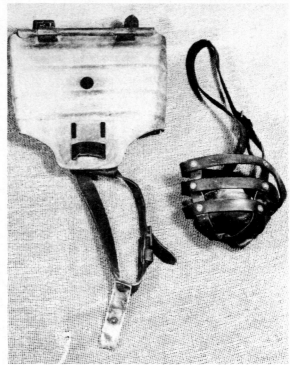

ABOVE: *A copper bull ring and two bull nose punches, used to make the hole between the bull's nostrils where the ring was inserted. The left-hand punch was simply made at a local smithy. The much grander punch on the right is the product of an urban veterinary instrument maker.*

RIGHT: *A metal bull blind (left), supposed to calm an aggressive bull on the principle that it would not charge if it could not see, and a horse's night muzzle (right), designed to prevent crib-biting.*

large disc was cut out of stiff cardboard or linoleum. In the centre was cut a hole large enough to fit the patient's neck snugly. The disc was then cut from outer edge to centre hole and laceholes were punched along either side of the cut. Known as an *Elizabethan frill* or *collar*, it was placed around the neck and laced tightly, making it impossible for the wearer to worry any wound on its flank.

A vicious or unpredictable dog would have its jaws immobilised before treatment. This was normally done by forming a length of bandage or some other material into a simple clove hitch, which was secured behind the head.

ABOVE: *A pig restrained by looping a rope round its upper mandible.*

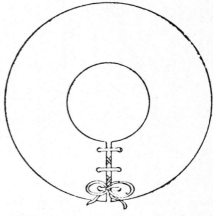

ABOVE: *An Elizabethan frill or collar, fitted to dogs and cats to prevent them from worrying wounds on their bodies.*

ABOVE: *A dog muzzled with a simple clove hitch secured behind the head.*

OPPOSITE TOP: *The lyre-shaped mouth gag (top) was used to hold a horse's mouth open while pills (boluses) were being administered. The gag was placed in the animal's mouth and conjunction with the flexible probang for removing obstructions from the animal's throat. The gag was placed in the animal's mouth and the probang was passed through the hole in the wood.*

OPPOSITE BOTTOM: *Sheep retaining yokes made from natural forks of timber, the left from maple and the right from ash. The sheep's head was placed in the fork and the wooden peg was slid through the holes so that the animal could not withdraw its head. The shepherd could then treat the animal as necessary.*

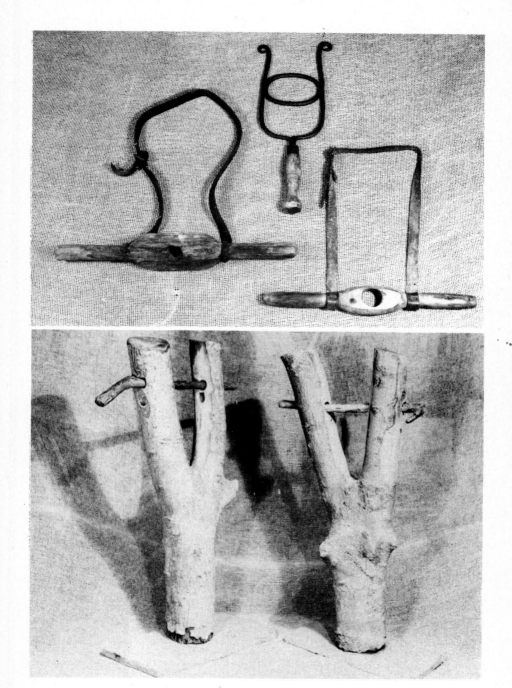

11

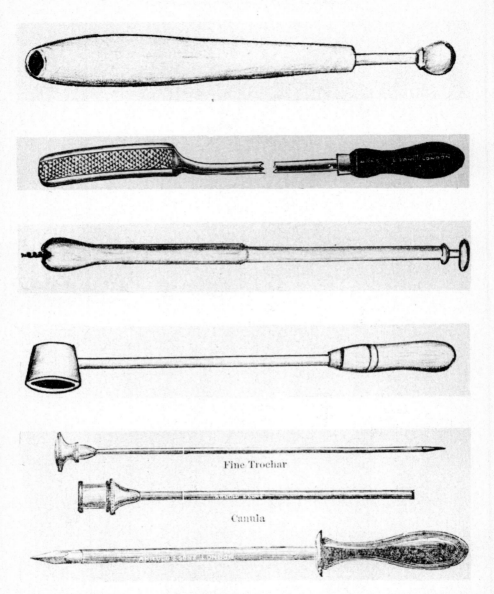

Fine Trochar

Canula

(From the top). A balling gun, used to propel a bolus to the back of a horse's mouth; a tooth rasp (shown with shaft shortened), for grinding down malformed or overgrown teeth which might prevent a horse masticating its food properly and so upset its digestion; a stilet probang, thrust down a cow's throat to spear and remove an obstruction; a hollow cauterising iron, used after the docking of a horse's tail to sear the flesh without injuring the vertebrae; the trochar and canula, a steel spike in a tubular shaft, were plunged into the distended abdomen of a cow or sheep, then the spike (trochar) was removed, leaving the canula (tube) in position for the gases to escape through.

A variety of drenching horns used to administer liquid medicines to cattle and sheep, and a toeless boot, used for the same purpose with pigs.

TREATMENT

Today sophisticated drugs unknown to nineteenth-century animal doctors are swiftly administered with a jab of the hypodermic needle, but formerly medicines for internal disorders had to be administered orally. With cattle, sheep and pigs this was normally done by mixing powders in the food, but horses are more fastidious and would frequently reject food so treated. Drugs were generally administered to horses in the form of large pills known as balls or boluses. Usually cylindrical in shape, about 2 inches long (50mm) and weighing around 1 ounce (28g), they were formed by mixing the powdered drug with linseed meal and some sticky substance such as treacle. The bolus was then moulded to the desired shape and size. The horse's mouth was wedged open with a *mouth gag*, a lyre-shaped metal instrument, some 14 inches (350mm) in length, set in a wooden handle.

In the centre of the lyre shape was an oval metal ring. The forks of the lyre lay on either side of the muzzle, the oval ring keeping the horse's mouth agape. Through this aperture the operator placed his hand, dropping the bolus on the rear of the animal's tongue. The gag was then removed and the mouth held shut with a strap around the muzzle until the bolus was swallowed. There were two alternative methods to placing the bolus by hand. One was a *blow pipe*, in effect a large pea-shooter, which the operator introduced through the aperture; he then blew the pill to the back of the throat. The other was the *balling gun*, a hollow wooden cylinder inside which ran a metal rod set at its upper end into a wooden handle. This was also placed through the aperture, where a sharp thrust of the rod propelled the bolus to the back of the throat.

Boluses were also occasionally given to

13

cattle and sheep, but a favoured way of administering medicines to these animals was the drench. Most medicines could be mixed into a liquid drench, which was particularly advantageous where large volumes were required. Sheep could be fairly readily handled. Cattle, however, needed to be restrained with the bulldog mentioned earlier, the head being raised so that the gullet was straight. Some stockmen dispensed with the bulldog and held the head aloft, gripping the nostrils with thumb and forefinger. Many purpose-designed bottles appeared for administering drenches, but nothing surpassed the *drenching horn* in effectiveness. This was the horn of a cow, in some cases cut to an oblique angle at its base to form a lip, in others bunged at its base with a disc of wood, and with its tip cut off to produce a smaller aperture. The drench was poured from the horn down the gullet. Sheep were treated likewise. Horses were also drenched, but with more caution because of their smaller gullet. Drenching pigs was always difficult, because they were awkward to handle and easily choked. A favoured way was to use an old boot with the toe cut off. The boot was forced into the mouth, whereupon the pig began chewing at it. The pigman then poured the drench slowly into the top of the boot and the pig almost unconsciously imbibed it.

Overshot or malformed teeth often caused problems, particularly in horses. They caused difficulty in masticating food and so upset the delicately balanced digestive system. These conditions were normally rectified by use of a *tooth rasp*, a short rasp, some 3 inches (75mm) long, surmounting a slender shaft set in a wooden handle. Badly overgrown teeth occasionally required cutting off with a chisel.

Cattle, particularly those grazing in orchards in autumn or being fed on chopped roots, were liable to blockages in the throat, resulting in choking. Such blockages had to be removed quickly. In early days stockmen attempted to impale the obstruction on the point of a slender stick thrust down the gullet or to dislodge it with a cart-whip, often causing a rupture of the animal's oesophagus. In the mid nineteenth century a professional-looking implement, which was even more of a hazard to the hapless animal, came into use. Called a *stilet probang*, it was a rigid, telescoping shaft some 3 feet (900mm) long, which was thrust down the throat. Running the length of the shaft and protruding from the tip was a corkscrew device which could be manipulated from the handle end. The object was to skewer the obstruction and withdraw it. The dire mishaps resulting from such an exercise can well be

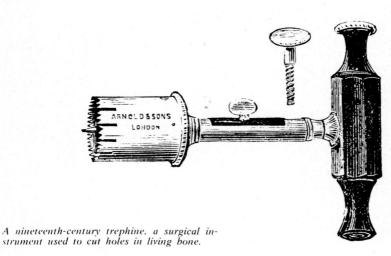

A nineteenth-century trephine, a surgical instrument used to cut holes in living bone.

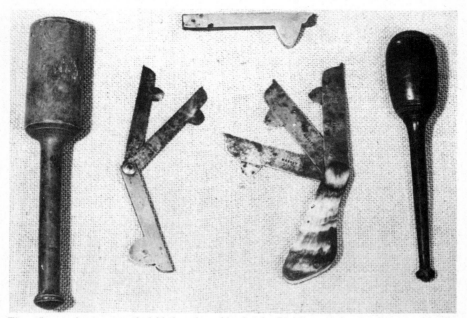

Three fleams, the top example folded, and two bloodsticks. Bleeding a sick animal was considered to be an effective cure for many ailments. To do this a blade of the fleam was placed on the chosen vein and given a sharp blow with the bloodstick.

imagined. Later in the nineteenth century a flexible probang was introduced. The shaft was about 6 feet 6 inches (2m) in length and made of coiled steel sheathed in leather. Through its core ran a flexible wooden rod attached to a handle at the top end. When the instrument had been inserted the operator attempted to push the blockage down by manipulating the rod. Although far from foolproof, it was a great improvement on the stilet. Modern equivalents are still occasionally used today. The wooden *cattle gag* was used in conjunction with both types of probang. It was a bar of wood about 18 inches (450mm) long fashioned into a handle at either end. A hole large enough to accommodate the head of the probang was bored in its centre. The gag was wedged into the beast's mouth and leather straps running from both handles were secured behind its poll. The probang was then introduced through the central hole.

Overeating wet luxuriant clover, rape or frosted turnips often produced in cattle and sheep a condition known as hoven, blown or tympanites, in which the left side of the abdomen became greatly distended with gases. A mixture of linseed and castor oils was considered efficacious, but in severe cases more drastic action was required to reduce internal pressures rapidly. Old stockmen would simply plunge their clasp knife into the animal's rumen, allowing the gases to escape. However, a more sophisticated instrument was marketed for use in such situations. This was the *trochar and canula*. The trochar was a steel spike about 8 inches (200mm) in length (although this was variable), set in a 4 inch (100 mm) wooden handle. Fitting the shaft of the spike exactly was the canula, a metal sleeve with a collar at the handle end. The instrument was plunged into the distended rumen and the trochar was removed, leaving the canula to act as a vent for the escaping gases.

It was sometimes necessary to remove discs of living bone, to treat an abscess in an animal's facial sinuses, to remove areas of necrosed bone or to destroy hydatids on the brain. This was performed with a *trepan* or a *trephine*. The trepan is an ancient instrument. Used rather like a carpenter's gimlet, it did not bore a hole but sawed one with a sleeve edged with cutting teeth. The trephine was a nineteenth-century variation using a central pin to guide the tool more accurately.

Bleeding domestic animals was much practised, as it was believed to be a certain remedy for all manner of ailments. However, by the end of the nineteenth century it was used much less widely and for only a few conditions, such as staggers in horses and cattle caused by overgorging on rich food, megrims, an accumulation of blood on the brain, and laminitis, an inflammation of the sensitive laminae inside the hoof. The instrument used in blood letting could be either the familiar surgeon's lancet or a *fleam*. The fleam resembled a pocket-knife with two or three blades, but the folding blades were not sharpened the length of one edge. Each terminated in a small triangular blade, honed razor-sharp on two facets, the blades being graduated in size. Used with the fleam was the *bloodstick*, a small clublike device about 7 to 10 inches (175 to 250mm) long, turned from some dense wood such as box and often loaded with lead. In order to bleed a horse its jugular vein was raised, either with the thumbs or with a cord tied around the neck. The chosen blade of the fleam was placed against the raised vein and given a sharp blow with the bloodstick or the side of a clenched fist. A pail was then placed to collect the blood; this was important as it enabled the amount taken to be gauged. The animal's lower jaw was often worked to speed the flow. When enough blood had been let the wound was drawn together with a pin, and a length of tow or hair from the horse's mane was wound round it in a figure of eight. Minor local bleeding to remove inflammation from eyes, etc, was also carried out. Cattle were frequently bled from a vein at the inside top of the leg.

A curious disease of cattle and sheep, similar to anthrax and called variously black quarter, black leg, quarter ill or pook, was treated in a strange way. Bacteria from the soil entered abrasions in the skin causing unsightly fluid swellings, deteriorating condition and eventual death. Certain areas of farmland, particularly in marshy districts have been known for generations as black-leg areas. The traditional precaution adopted with cattle dates back perhaps hundreds of years and is called *setoning*. Tape smeared with a blistering substance was threaded through the dewlap, using a *seton needle*. This caused much swelling and the formation of matter, which it was believed carried off toxic fluid. The success rate in many areas was claimed to be very high. A simpler expedient was used by some stockmen. They believed that a goat running with the herd would ward off the condition.

The docking of horses' tails was at one time fashionable but is now fortunately outlawed for all but strictly veterinary purposes. The implement used to dock tails was a *tail-docking iron*. It was a hand-operated guillotine, similar to a pair of nutcrackers, with two handles joined by a pivot. The top handle was attached to a semicircular blade, the bottom handle to a wooden block in which was carved a deep hollow holding a narrow groove and designed to receive the blade with a precise fit. The tail of the horse was placed in the hollow and sharp pressure was applied on the top handle, forcing the blade into the groove and severing the tail. Some models were mounted on a stand, where the bottom handle was replaced by a block but the hollow and groove were retained. The open wound was then cauterised with a *hollow cauterising iron* to prevent infection. This was a heavy hollowed ring of iron about 2 inches (50mm) across surmounting a long shaft set in a wooden handle.

Lambs were docked with a device also called a docking iron, but this implement docked and cauterised in one movement and would be more correctly termed a *searing iron*. It had a square spade-like head 2 to 3 inches (50 to 75mm) wide on a long metal shaft normally set in a wooden handle. The lamb's tail was laid on a stone or iron block. The iron, heated red-hot, was placed on the tail and with the aid of slight pressure was allowed to sear through between the vertebrae. Lambs were also docked with clasp knives and by tying the

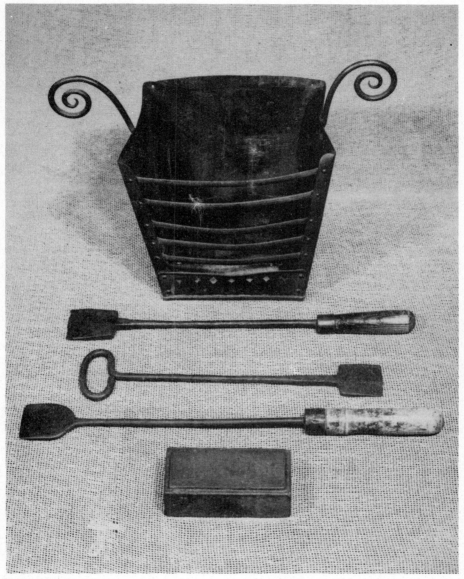

Three sheep's tail-docking irons, a block and a brazier for heating the irons. The tail was placed on the block and the red-hot iron positioned on it, searing through it with the application of slight pressure.

tail with string to constrict the blood supply, allowing the lower portion to become slowly necrosed. Many countrymen boasted of biting off the tails of lambs and puppies. Doubtless this did happen but was more boasted of than performed.

Castration was carried out on young male stock not required for breeding as it was thought to induce docility and enhance fattening propensities. It was usually carried out in early summer. On colts as yearlings it could be performed either with the animal standing or cast. The normal method was to release the testes from the scrotum with either a *castrating knife* or hot *castrating iron.* Castrating clamps were then attached to the cord to produce insensibility in the organ. The cord was then severed with the hot castrating iron, cauterising the wound. A mixture of verdigris, Venice turpentine and lard was smeared liberally around the wound. Ligatures were also used to constrict the spermatic cord and by the turn of the century an instrument called an *ecraseur,* which crushed the cord, had been introduced. Calves were castrated in the same way as colts but usually much earlier, at an age of six to twelve weeks. Lambs were castrated at between three weeks and three months. One man held the lamb in a sitting posture, its back to his chest, while a second man cut an inch or so from the base of the scrotum, exposing the testes, which he then drew out with a pair of *castrating forceps.* There are, however, many authenticated instances of shepherds doing this with their teeth.

Many problems were encountered at parturition, perhaps the most common being that of the turned calf, foal or lamb, where the foetus was incorrectly positioned in the womb. Head and front legs foremost was the natural position of presentation, but the foetus could be in one of a number of positions. The foetus had to be turned and the head and limbs manipulated into the correct position. This was often a protracted and arduous task with a cow or mare, performed by strength of hand and arm alone, although ropes were often used, with caution, for added leverage. Many other aids were gradually devised. A loop of cord on a rod, similar in appearance to a twitch and called a *porte-cord,* was often used, as were various *hooks* or *crotchets* attached to the rope. Around the turn of the century a set of aids called Gowings Parturition Instrument appeared. These were various crooks, levers and rods which screwed into a master handle called the crutch or repeller. Lambs were more easily turned by hand, but the shepherd occasionally used a pair of *obstetrical forceps.* A similar pair of forceps was used with bitches experiencing a difficult whelping. The treatment for infections in the womb after parturition and the administration of enemas were normally carried out with a sturdy brass-barrelled syringe called a *clyster pump.* Various ebony pipes could be fitted for use with horses, cattle, sheep or dogs.

An ancient practice employed in curing lameness in horses was *firing.* A simple and seemingly cruel treatment, it was thought to relieve the deep-seated inflammation responsible for the lameness by exciting pain in more superficial parts.

The ecraseur, introduced around 1900 for castrating colts, crushed and severed the spermatic cord in one operation.

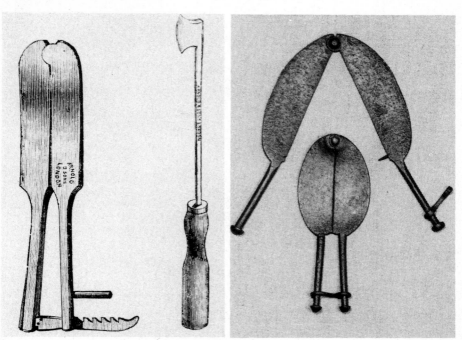

ABOVE LEFT: *A castrating iron (right) was used red-hot to sear the scrotum, after which the pair of castrating clamps (left) were attached to produce insensibility in the organ.*
ABOVE RIGHT: *Two pairs of early castrating clamps with crude clip closure.*
BELOW: *A castrating knife and a pair of castrating forceps used with lambs.*

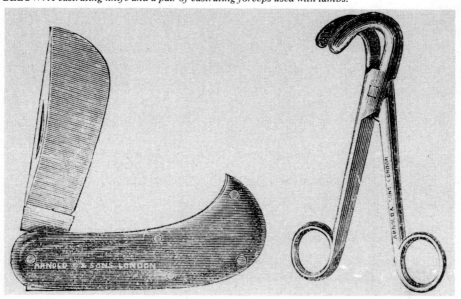

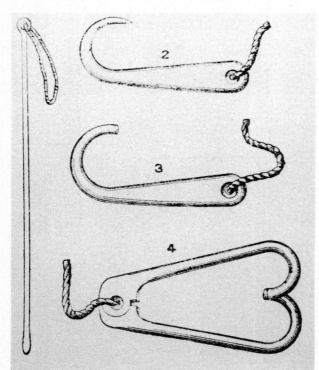

LEFT: *A porte-cord (left, not to scale) and three crotchets (from top: sharp, blunt and double) used with ropes to aid manipulation of a turned foetus.*

BELOW: *A clyster pump, used to administer enemas and to treat infected wombs after parturition.*
BOTTOM: *Gowings Parturition Instrument, designed so that the various attachments screwed into the master crutch or repeller, as in the topmost example.*

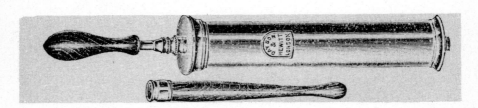

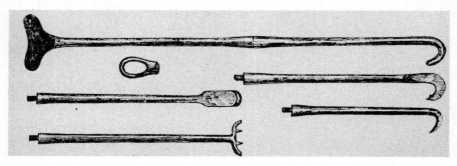

The hair was closely clipped from the area to be fired and the horse was cast. The *firing iron*, a heavy edged blade surmounting a wooden-handled metal shaft, was heated in coals until red-hot. It was then drawn in parallel lines over the clipped area, lightly searing the flesh. Towards the end of the 1900s chloroform was normally administered to relieve suffering, and firing slowly gave way to the use of *blistering creams*, which produced much the same results.

The farrier was to many country folk not only the shoer of their horses but also the doctor of their stock. Indeed shoeing is basically a veterinary art. The leather-aproned farrier clutching a horse's hind hoof between his thighs is a familiar picture but this was not so easily done with the foreleg, where the farrier often used a metal *shoeing tripod* on which to rest the foot. Before the new shoe was fitted, the old had to be removed. Here the farrier used a *clenching iron*, a double-headed implement, one end formed to a chisel blade, the other to a point. He used the chisel end with a hammer to cut off the clenches or clints, the bent-over sections of nail protruding through the hoof wall and holding the shoe in place. This done, the nails were withdrawn with his pincers and the worn shoe was removed. The hoof had then to be prepared to receive the new shoe. In heavy working horses the area in the centre of the hoof around the sensitive

'frog' often became clogged with detritus, which was removed with a small trowel-like tool called a *buttress knife*. The final trimming and cleaning was done with two other, finer knives, the *hoof-paring knife* and the *searcher*. The paring knife could also be used on the outer surface of the hoof to trim excess horn in conjunction with the *hoof rasp*. When horses were left on grass for long periods without being shod, the hooves could become very overshot, requiring the removal of much horn. This operation was carried out with a *bolster* or *buffer*, a small cleaver-shaped tool which chopped through the horn when struck with a hammer. The hoof was thus prepared for re-shoeing.

Hot shoeing was considered superior to cold shoeing. The hot shoe was taken from the coals with the tongs and allowed to burn a seat on the hoof, although many farriers preferred to handle the hot shoe by placing a *pritchell*, a spike-shaped chisel, in a nail hole. The shoe thus seated was quenched to cool, then nailed on. For this the farrier used specially malleable wire nails and his *shoeing hammer*, a narrow-faced hammer with claw head. The nails were skilfully driven to emerge from the outer wall of the hoof, where the points were deftly bent over and twisted off by use of the hammer claw.

The hooves of other animals were often trimmed but this required the use of only the paring knife, hoof rasp and oc-

Flat and cone bladed firing irons. Searing the flesh with irons like these was thought to relieve deep-seated inflammation.

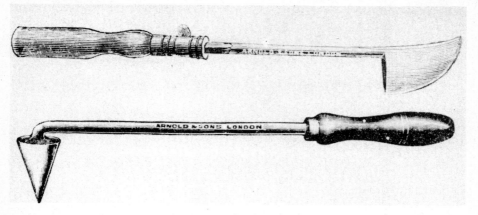

casionally the bolster. Working oxen and cattle driven for long distances by road were also shod in a similar manner to horses, but they required two crescent-shaped shoes on each hoof to allow for spread of the clove.

The farrier was also called upon to produce surgical horseshoes to rectify foot ailments. Another appliance used for this purpose was made not by the farrier but by the harness maker. It was a *poultice boot*, a large leather and canvas overshoe, used when a horse suffered from a foot abscess. It had a stout leather sole and upper to the level of the hoof coronet. Above this it was heavy canvas supported by leather straps, ending a short distance above the fetlock. It was filled with hot bran and strapped on to the affected foot to draw the abscess. A similar type of boot, but much smaller and without the hot bran, was sometimes fitted to sheep suffering from foot rot, but it was generally agreed that this was an abject failure.

A farrier's shoeing tools arranged in front of his toolbox, in which they were always carried: (top) pincers; (bottom) a hoof rasp; (from left to right) a buttress knife, two clenching irons and a searcher, a pritchell, two buffers or bolsters and a hoof-paring knife, a shoeing hammer.

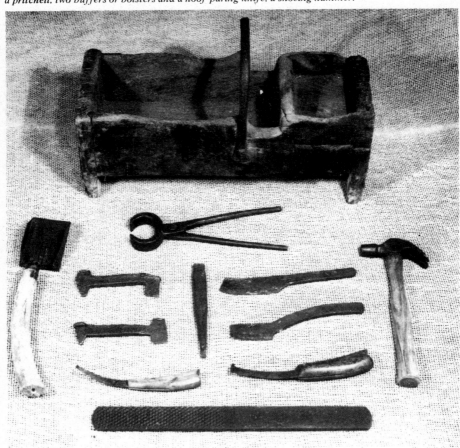

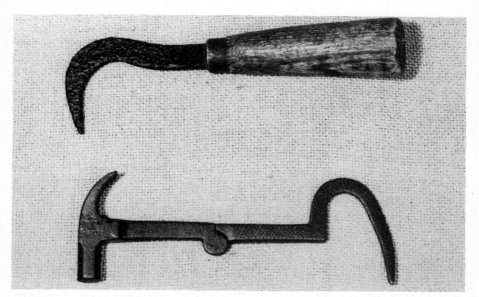

ABOVE: *A hoof pick, for removing stones wedged in the hoof, and a folding carter's companion, a tool with a hoof pick at one end and a tiny claw hammer at the other.*

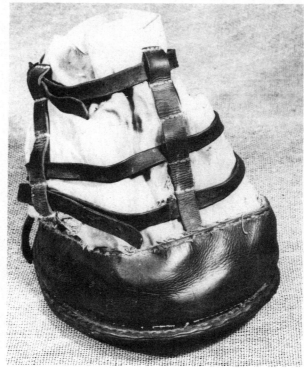

RIGHT: *A poultice boot for a heavy horse. Made by a harness maker, such a boot protected the foot if infected by an abscess.*

The *hoofpick*, a simple tool carried by the carter and ploughman, saved much veterinary work later. A curved piece of iron usually set in a wooden handle, it was used to hook out small stones wedged in the sole of the hoof, which if left could produce lameness. A sophistication was a *folding carter's tool*, which was hinged in the middle. One head was a hoofpick and the other a small claw-head hammer for knocking in or drawing out loose shoe-nails.

Another very simple tool preventing the need for veterinary attention was carried by the shepherd. It was the tiny *shepherd's saw*. About 6 inches (150mm) long, it was used to cut off the tips of horns in danger of growing into the eye socket or the skull.

Before sheep-dipping was widespread sheep were salved. Each sheep had its fleece laboriously parted and its skin smeared with a mixture of tar, butter, fish oil, goose grease and various other ingredients, according to individual preference. This was done to prevent scab and protect against parasites. Needing both hands to restrain the sheep and part the fleece, the shepherd had to overcome the problem of holding a supply of salve. So he used a cunningly made little wooden container which he strapped to his wrist. Called a *salve box*, it was carved in one piece and had a main box part to contain the salve and a small lip carved on one side to fit the ball of the thumb and enable the user to scrape off any excess. It was about 4 inches (100mm) long and was secured to the wrist by a broad leather strap or thongs.

It was quite common for dogs to have their ears cropped. This was often done with an instrument called a *hound rounding iron*, a metal chisel with a broad semicircular blade. The ear flap of the

A hound rounding iron (left), used to trim the ear flaps of hunting dogs to prevent them being torn by brambles, and a pair of curved scissors used to dub poultry, that is to remove the wattles and comb, particularly of birds used for cock fighting.

The shepherd's saw (left) was used for removing the tips of horns that were likely to grow in a contorted fashion, bending back to penetrate the sheep's head or eyes. The salve box (centre) was an ingenious device to help the shepherd apply salve to his sheep. By strapping the box to his wrist he ensured a supply of salve readily to hand, whilst leaving both hands free to restrain the sheep and part its fleece. The seton needle (right) was used for threading tape smeared with a blistering substance through the dewlaps of cattle. This was intended to ward off the disease known as black quarter, prevalent amongst animals grazing in marshy areas.

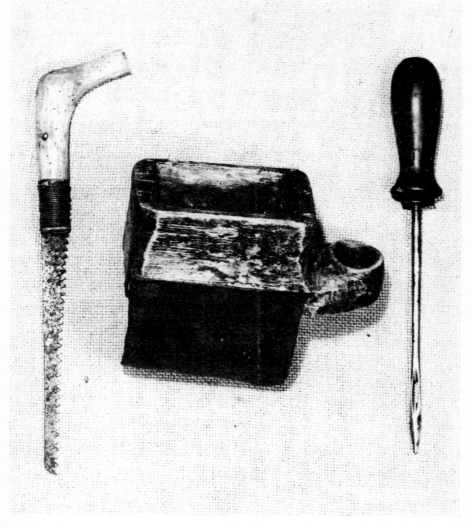

unfortunate dog was placed on a block. The iron was placed on it and given a sharp blow with a mallet. This was done to hunting dogs to reduce the area of ear flap likely to be torn by thorn and briar and also to fighting dogs destined for the pit, before that became illegal. Fighting cocks intended for the pit were likewise treated by having combs and wattles dubbed. This was also practised in many barnyards, the dubbing being performed with a curved pair of scissors.

Three devices quite widely used by the stockman were horn trainers, horn crowners and anti-suckling muzzles and collars. *Horn trainers* were used when cattle were prized almost as much for their appearance as for their beef or milk yield and a pair of perfectly symmetrical horns was considered an essential feature. There were three main types of horn trainers. One consisted of two lead pods, which slipped over the tips of the horns. These were joined by two leather straps which could be tightened as necessary to induce correct horn growth. Another type was normally made of iron. Again two pods or

cups fitted over the tips of the horns but these were joined by two threaded metal bars which could be regulated by tightening two nuts. The third type was of wooden construction and strapped on behind the horns. Two leather-lined flaps were hinged and by means of wooden threads could be screwed forwards. This type could be used to induce only the forward growth of the horns.

The *horn crowner* was a two-handled metal clamp used to retain brass horn butts in a vice-like grip whilst screwing them on to the horn tips. A screw thread running inside the butt reamed a thread on the horn as it was turned. Brass butts were fitted partly for aesthetic reasons but also to prevent sharp horn tips inflicting damage on other members of the herd.

Many young stock continue to suckle milking mothers long after the stockman desires it, and many older animals re-establish the habit. To combat this, the offending animal was fitted with an *anti-suckling muzzle*. This was simply a leather halter, the noseband of which was studded with metal spikes, although in some areas

A horn crowner with brass butt secured in position. It held the butts tightly while they were being fitted to a cow's horns.

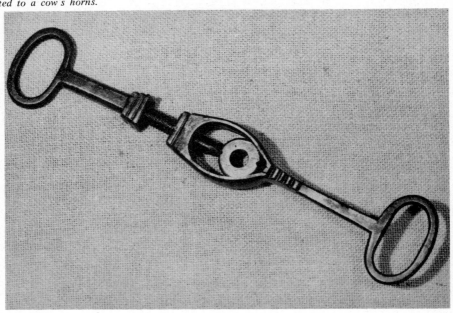

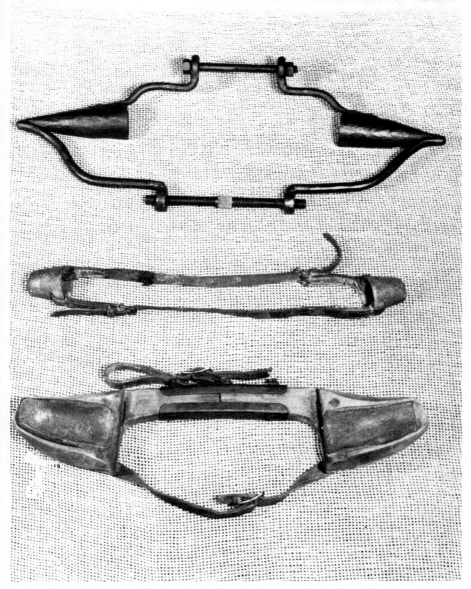

Horn trainers for cattle: (top) made of iron, adjustable by a metal screw thread; (centre) made of lead, adjustable by leather straps; (bottom) made of wood, adjustable from the rear by wooden threads. This example was strapped behind the horns, but the other two fitted directly on to them.

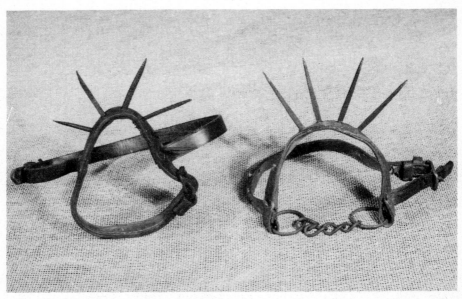

Anti-suckling muzzles for cattle. Such devices were fitted to young animals to prevent them from suckling after the stockman wished them to stop.

a studded leather neck collar was used. When the animal attempted to suckle another cow, the device was effective for obvious reasons.

In addition to these multifarious instruments and devices the vet, stockman, farrier, shepherd, cottager, carter and cad used innumerable concoctions, medicines and remedies, some effective but many useless. Most were homespun, but many were sold under brand names.

There existed on the fringe of the veterinary field an art shrouded in mystery and discussed with much reticence. The art was that of the horse whisperer. These characters, and they were few, had the power to calm and control wild and truculent horses. They could stop a horse, apparently compliant to its handler, in its tracks, so that nothing would induce it to move. Then at the whisperer's bidding it would proceed just as suddenly upon its way. Country folk believed these powers were derived from performing a peculiar rite with a natterjack toad. The toad was killed and hung on a whitethorn bush for a full day, then buried in an anthill until all the flesh had been removed from the bones. The skeleton was then removed at full moon and dropped into a stream. One bone, usually the pelvic bone, would detach itself from the rest and float against the current. This bone was gathered up, baked, crushed, mixed with a pungent oil and carried about the person. In reality these charlatans concocted certain mixtures. These varied, but one was a mixture of oil of origanum, oil of rosemary, oil of cinnamon and oil of fennel. They smeared it on the horse's muzzle or forequarters. A few masticated the mixture, breathing it into the animal's nostrils. After this the horse became calmed. Smearing some of the substance on his own person, the whisperer could attract the horse to him. This was known as drawing a horse. Stopping a horse in its tracks was called jading and was usually done by surreptitiously smearing on the horse's chest an obnoxious smell such as musk from the scent glands of a ferret. The horse, finding the smell repellent,

28

A selection of proprietary brands of Victorian animal medicines: (front) Day & Sons Black Drink, claimed to cure fret, colic, gripes and fits in horses, hoven, blown and scours in cattle, diarrhoea, weakness and exhaustion after lambing in sheep; (others from left) Pinkstones Curchiline — 'cures cattle diseases'; Benbows Dog Mixture; Tippers Vitalis, claimed to cure, amongst other things, inflammation of the lungs, overdone, flatulent colic, blown, distemper, roup in poultry and snuffles in rabbits; a block of Osmonds Greasewash, 'the old Lincolnshire cure for grease' (a chronic inflammation of working horses' legs); Gregory & Co's Hosdrink, for gripes; Ellimans Royal Embrocation for horses.

A splendid Victorian advertisement for Tippers animal medicines. Note particularly the butt of the discerning bull's wrath — the tattered box of 'quack medicines, worthless imitations'.

would refuse to move forward. The whisperer would then, for a small consideration, offer his services. He would rub the area with a hand covered in milk and vinegar. This neutralised the smell and the horse would then happily proceed.

Veterinary science has advanced enormously over the past fifty years and today stands on a par with human medicine. However, there are few modern vets who would guarantee to calm an unruly horse, even using all his modern instruments, much less with the pelvic bone of a natterjack toad.

FURTHER READING

Brown, T. *The Complete Modern Farrier.* Grant, 1898.

Stephens, Henry. *Book of the Farm* (various editions and volumes). Blackwood & Sons, 1836 to 1900.

Wright, Professor R. Patrick. *The Standard Cyclopedia of Modern Agriculture.* Gresham, 1908.

The Key to Farriery (or Veterinary Practice at Home). Day, Son & Hewett, 1896.

PLACES TO VISIT

Breamore Countryside Museum, Breamore House, Fordingbridge, Hampshire (tel. Breamore 233).

Castle Farm Folk Museum, Marshfield (Avon), Chippenham, Wiltshire (tel. Marshfield 469).

Cotswold Folk and Agricultural Museum, c/o Andrews Cottage, Asthall Barrow, Burford, Oxfordshire (tel. Burford 2178).

Cricket St Thomas Wildlife Park, near Chard, Somerset.

Dorset County Museum, Dorchester, Dorset (tel. Dorchester 2735).

James Countryside Museum, Bicton Gardens, East Budleigh, Devon (tel. Budleigh Salterton 3881).

Museum of East Anglian Life, Abbots Hall, Stowmarket, Suffolk (tel. Stowmarket 2229).

Museum of English Rural Life, University of Reading, Whiteknights Park, Reading, Berkshire (tel. Reading 85123 ext. 475).

North of England Open Air Museum, Beamish Hall, Beamish, Stanley, Co. Durham (tel. Stanley 33580 or 33586).

Norton's Farm Museum, Kent Street, Sedlescombe, Battle, East Sussex (tel. Sedlescombe 471).

Oxfordshire County Museum, Fletcher's House, Woodstock, Oxfordshire (tel. Woodstock 811456).

Rutland County Museum, Catmos Street, Oakham, Leicestershire (tel. Oakham 3654).

Ryedale Folk Museum, Hutton-le-Hole, North Yorkshire (tel. Lastingham 367).

Steam and Countryside Museum, Sandy Bay, Exmouth, Devon.

The White House Country Life Museum, Aston Munslow, Salop.

Weald and Downland Open Air Museum, Singleton, near Chichester, West Sussex (tel. Singleton 348).

Welsh Folk Museum, St Fagans, Cardiff, South Glamorgan (tel. Cardiff 561357 or 561358).

West Yorkshire Folk Museum, Shibden Hall, Halifax, West Yorkshire (tel. Elland 2540).

Weyhill Wildlife Park and Rural Life Museum, Weyhill, Andover, Hampshire (tel. Weyhill 2252).

ACKNOWLEDGEMENTS

The author acknowledges with gratitude the help received from the following in the preparation of this book: Mr Barry Fowler; Mr Malcom Harris; Mrs Ruth Ingram; Mr Murdoch Mactaggart; Mrs Kathleen Wiltshire.